Grammar
Practice Book

Grade 3

Harcourt

Orlando   Boston   Dallas   Chicago   San Diego

Visit *The Learning Site!*
www.harcourtschool.com

ISBN 0-15-312701-5

1 2 3 4 5 6 7 8 9 10   022   2002 2001 2000 99

Contents

Contents

To the Student

Did you know that the English language is both old and new? English has a long history. It has grown from many languages. New words are added all the time. English is always growing and changing.

dictionary—Latin

alligator—Spanish

pizza—Italian

muskrat—Native American

Internet—new word

We hear and use many kinds of English. People who live in different places speak English in different ways. They may use different words for the same thing. They may pronounce the same word in different ways.

Would you call this a paper bag or a paper sack?
Do you drink water from a water fountain or a bubbler?

We often need a kind of English that everyone agrees on. That kind of English is called Standard English. It is used in schools, in businesses, and on television newscasts.

The grammar you will use in this book is Standard English. You probably already know a lot about Standard English and use it often. This book will help you remember to use it when you write. It will also help you name the parts of speech and the parts of sentences you use. Using these names will help you when you talk about your writing. You will find a list of the parts of speech on the next page.

Harcourt

Introduction

Parts of Speech

Noun

A noun names a person, a place, a thing, or an idea.

Becca took a **book** to her **brother.**

Pronoun

A pronoun takes the place of a noun.

She took **it** to **him.**

Adjective

An adjective describes a noun.

The **small** child petted the **friendly** cat.

Verb

A verb expresses action or being.

The cat **closed** its eyes and **purred.**

The cat **was** happy.

Adverb

An adverb describes a verb.

The dog barked **loudly.**

Harcourt

Skill Reminder

- **A sentence** tells a complete thought. It names someone or something and tells what that person or thing is or does.
- **Words in a sentence are in an order that makes sense.**
- **A sentence always begins with a capital letter and ends with an end mark.**

▶ **Read each group of words. Write** *sentence* **or** *not a sentence*.

   1. A funny story about elephants. _____

   2. D. W. had a good story idea. _____

   3. Arthur should tell about his puppy. _____

   4. Reading books in the library. _____

   5. Was the Brain's story interesting? _____

▶ **Rewrite these sentences. Put the words in an order that makes sense. Begin with a capital letter and end with an end mark. Find one word that always needs to be written with a capital letter. Circle it.**

   6. a Buster notebook has.

_____

   7. like you Buster's did story?

_____

   8. enjoyed story his very much i.

_____

▶ **This story tells how Arthur and D. W. made lemonade one day. Read the paragraph below. The first sentence is missing. Write a good first sentence for the story.**

Making Lemonade

1. _____

_____

D. W. and Arthur squeezed about 100 lemons. Then they added sugar and water. D. W. stirred the lemonade with a spoon and tasted it.

▶ **Here's more of Arthur's story. But the sentences do not make sense. Rewrite them so they make sense.**

2. too it sour was.

_____

3. sugar added they more.

_____

▶ **Finish Arthur's story by adding words to these word groups. Write two complete sentences to tell what happened next.**

4. Arthur tasted

_____

5. Finally just right

_____

Sentences; Capitalization

Harcourt

▶ Read each group of words. If it is a sentence, write
sentence on the line below. If it is not a sentence, add words to make it
complete. Write your sentence on the line. Be sure to begin with a
capital letter and end with an end mark.

1. the first story.

_____

2. Arthur's friends found the story boring.

_____

3. sang and danced his second story.

_____

4. Did you find the story confusing?

_____

5. the other children.

_____

▶ Rewrite each sentence. Put the words in an order that makes sense.
Begin each sentence with a capital letter and end with an end mark.

6. dog i wanted always a.

_____

7. business opened a pet arthur.

_____

8. lot was a work of it.

_____

9. lose Arthur did a dog?

_____

10. the puppies one he kept of.

_____

Sentences; Capitalization

Name _____

Skill Reminder

• **A statement** is a sentence that tells something. Use a period (.) to end a statement.
• **A question** is a sentence that asks something. Use a question mark (?) to end a question.

▶ Decide what kind of sentence each one is. Add the correct end mark for each. Then write *statement* or *question*.

1. Do you jump rope __   _____

2. I like to jump rope __   _____

3. Here are two ropes __   _____

4. How many times did you jump __   _____

5. I won the game __   _____

▶ Add the correct end mark to each sentence. Then rewrite each sentence. Change each statement into a question. Change each question into a statement. Be sure to begin with a capital letter.

6. The girls are jumping rope __

   _____

7. Are the twins playing __

   _____

8. Can we play Double Dutch __

   _____

9. Tanya will turn the rope __

   _____

10. Is Vanya a great jumper __

   _____

Harcourt

▶ Rosa and Marta are telling their parents what happened to Colleen's key. Finish the sentences in the cartoon balloons. Add end punctuation.

▶ Add words to the cartoon balloons. Write complete statements or questions.

Harcourt

▶ **Add words to make these word groups complete sentences. Write the sentences. Begin each one with a capital letter. End with the correct end mark.**

1. kept kicking the can

_____

2. the smell of chicken soup

_____

3. stuck on the refrigerator

_____

4. a baby laughing

_____

5. pulled the string up

_____

▶ **Add the correct end mark to these sentences.**

6. Marta's family moved __

7. Rosa kept her side of the room clean __

8. Did Marta bring her collections with her __

9. Rosa has a new friend __

10. Will Marta make some new friends __

Sentences; Statements and Questions

Harcourt

Name _____

Skill Reminder

• A **command** is a sentence that gives an order or a direction. End a command with a period (.).

• An **exclamation** is a sentence that shows strong feeling. End an exclamation with an exclamation point (!).

▶ Tell what kind of sentence each one is. Circle *command* or *exclamation*. Then add the correct end mark.

1. Feed that duck some crumbs _   command   exclamation

2. What a loud quack he has _   command   exclamation

3. How pretty his feathers are _   command   exclamation

4. Please take his picture _   command   exclamation

5. Wow, he's flapping his wings _   command   exclamation

▶ Rewrite these sentences. Begin each with a capital letter and add the correct end mark.

6. hold this snake carefully

_____

7. what a loud hiss it makes

_____

8. be gentle with it

_____

9. what soft skin snakes have

_____

10. put it back into the weeds

_____

Name_____

▶ **Ronald is going home from camp. Find the
exclamations and commands. Write the kind of sentence
each one is. Add the correct end mark for each sentence.**

1. Ronald: What a good time I had _____   _____

2. Father: Please help me load the car _____   _____

3. Father: Get in the car, everyone _____   _____

4. Aunt Ruth: My, what a long trip it is _____   _____

5. Mother: Look at the map, Ronald _____   _____

6. Ronald: Hooray, I see our town _____   _____

▶ **Continue the scene. Write a sentence for each person. Use the kind of
sentence named in parentheses ( ).**

7. Mother: (exclamation)

_____

8. Father: (command)

_____

9. Ronald: (exclamation)

_____

10. Aunt Ruth: (command)

_____

Commands and Exclamations

▶ Write *sentence* beneath each complete sentence.
Rewrite the other word groups, adding words to make them complete sentences.

1. The camping trip.

_____

2. I gave her some raisins.

_____

3. Gave the duck a cracker.

_____

4. Practiced my song.

_____

5. We rolled down the hill.

_____

▶ Add the correct end mark to each sentence. Write *statement*, *question*, *command*, or *exclamation* to tell what kind of sentence it is.

6. I surprised two rabbits in the field _   _____

7. Are there many rabbits here _   _____

8. Shoo them away, Dave _   _____

9. How floppy their ears look _   _____

10. Please carry my pail for me _   _____

Sentences; Kinds of Sentences

Skill Reminder

• **A subject** tells who or what a sentence is about.
• **A predicate** tells what a subject is or does.

▶ **Draw one line under the subject.**

1. Allie's house is near the fire station.

2. Mr. Puchinsky is the fire captain.

3. He runs the fire station.

4. A fire captain has an important job.

5. Allie's father waves to the fire captain.

▶ **Draw two lines under the predicate.**

6. The little dog barks at Allie.

7. She gives him a biscuit.

8. The fire fighters like Domino.

9. He is friendly and helpful.

10. The dog plays with the children at the playground.

▶ **Read Allie's thank-you letter to her father. Draw one
line under the subject of each numbered sentence. Draw two lines
under each predicate.**

Dear Daddy,
  (1) I love my new
basketball. (2) You are
the best father in the world.
(3) My friends practiced in
the park today. (4) Every-
body had a good time.
(5) That brand-new
basketball got a real
workout.
        Love,
        Allie

▶ **Allie wrote about her basketball dream. Help her complete each
sentence. Add a subject or a predicate.**

6. Basketball _____

7. My father _____

8. _____ watched games on television.

9. _____ went to a professional game.

10. A good athlete _____

Harcourt

Name_____

▶ **Add the correct end mark to these sentences.**

1. Allie bounced the ball on the sidewalk _

2. What a nice sound it makes _

3. Can you shoot a basket _

4. Shoot some baskets with me _

▶ **Draw one line under the subject. Draw two lines under the predicate.**

5. Allie kicked the ball.

6. She aimed at the basket.

7. Allie's new basketball hit the backboard.

8. Julio liked the game of basketball.

▶ **Write one of each kind of sentence. Use the correct end mark for each sentence. Be sure each is a complete sentence.**

9. Statement _____

_____

10. Question _____

_____

11. Command _____

_____

12. Exclamation _____

_____

Complete Sentences; Kinds of Sentences;
Subjects and Predicates

Name _____

Skill Reminder

- **A compound subject** is two or more subjects that share a predicate.
- **A compound predicate** is two or more predicates that share a subject.
- Use commas to separate three or more subjects or predicates.

▶ Draw one line under each compound subject. Circle the word *and*. Add commas where they belong.

1. Amy and her teammates stayed at a hotel.

2. The coach and the team's doctor worked together.

3. Fans photographers and sportscasters are ready.

4. Amy her coach and the other Americans smile.

▶ Draw two lines under each compound predicate. Circle the word *and*. Add commas where they belong.

5. The United States picks good athletes and trains them well.

6. Amy breathes deeply stretches and hopes for the best.

7. She won a gold medal and broke a record!

8. The people in the stands cheer stamp and sing.

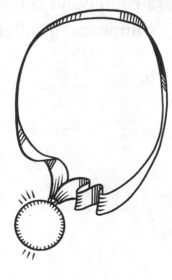

Compound Subjects and Predicates

Harcourt

Name_____

▶ **Rewrite each group of words to make it a complete sentence. Each sentence should have a compound subject or a compound predicate. Use the objects shown in the pictures to help you.**

1. my swim goggles

_____

2. the shovel and bucket

_____

3. walk along the beach

_____

4. swim underwater

_____

_____

▶ **Use the objects in the pictures to help you write sentences of your own. Write one sentence with a compound subject and one sentence with a compound predicate.**

5. _____

_____

6. _____

_____

▶ **Choose the best way to write each underlined section and fill in the oval for the correct answer. If the underlined section needs no change, mark the choice "No mistake."**

Amy Van Dyken overcame poor health and became a swimming champion. **(1)** One time she had to be carried off. On a stretcher. **(2)** What a disappointment that was! For a while she could not swim at all. **(3)** Amy and her coach worked out a plan. Her doctor worked out a plan, too. **(4)** She kept swimming. Won a bronze medal.

1 ⊂ One time she had to be carried off. While on a stretcher.

  ⊂ One time she had to be carried off, she was on a stretcher.

  ⊂ One time she had to be carried off on a stretcher.

  ⊂ No mistake

2 ⊂ what a disappointment that was

  ⊂ What a disappointment that was.

  ⊂ what a disappointment that was?

  ⊂ No mistake

3 ⊂ Amy and her coach, her doctor worked out a plan.

  ⊂ Amy her coach, and her doctor worked out a plan.

  ⊂ Amy, her coach, and her doctor worked out a plan.

  ⊂ No mistake

4 ⊂ She kept swimming and won a bronze medal.

  ⊂ She kept swimming she won a bronze medal.

  ⊂ She kept swimming. Winning a bronze medal.

  ⊂ No mistake

Harcourt

Complete Sentences; Kinds of Sentences, Compound Subjects and Predicates

Sentences
Statements and Questions
Commands and
Exclamations
Subjects and Predicates
Compound Subjects and
Predicates

Theme 1 Review

▶ **If the words make a sentence, write *sentence*.**
If they do not, write *not a sentence*.

1. Likes animal stories. _____

2. We wrote stories for our class. _____

3. Do you have a pet? _____

4. My kitten. _____

5. Built a birdhouse. _____

▶ **Write each sentence correctly. Then write *statement*, *question*, *command*, or *exclamation* after each sentence.**

6. do you have a hobby

   _____

7. hobbies can be great fun

   _____

8. pick up that marble

   _____

9. what a deep blue it is

   _____

10. i collect pictures of animals

    _____

11. what a long neck that giraffe has

    _____

12. where is your stamp album

    _____

Harcourt

Name_____

Theme 1 Review

▶ **Draw one line under the subject. Draw two lines under the predicate.**

13. Mark plays softball.

14. He throws the ball well.

15. My sister is on the team.

16. She hit a home run last week.

17. Rita is also a team member.

18. Both children are pitchers.

▶ **Underline the subject once and underline the predicate twice. Write _compound subject_ or _compound predicate_ to tell what the sentence has.**

19. Fred and Matt like gardening. _____

20. César has a camera and likes taking pictures. _____

21. Susan is an artist and paints every day. _____

22. César likes her paintings and photographs them.

_____

23. Michael and Roberta enjoy making pottery. _____

▶ **Write two sentences. Give one a compound subject. Give the other a compound predicate.**

24. _____

_____

25. _____

_____

Skill Reminder

• Use *and* or *but* to join two complete sentences into a **compound sentence.**

• Use a comma (,) before *and* or *but* when it joins sentences.

▶ Write each compound sentence correctly. Use a comma and the joining word *and* or *but*.

1. Gloria gave him a kiss and he gave her a pat.

_____

2. Officer Buckle thought of a safety tip, he was excited.

_____

3. Gloria is fine alone but she is better with Officer Buckle.

_____

4. Claire wrote a letter, Officer Buckle enjoyed it.

_____

5. Officer Buckle was popular but he did not know why.

_____

▶ Use proofreading marks to add commas to these sentences.

   Example: Officer Buckle was serious ⌄ but Gloria was funny.

6. The children liked the officer   but they liked Gloria more.

7. The students listened to the talk   and they cheered afterward.

8. Everyone enjoyed the talk   and we all learned about safety.

Harcourt

Name _____

Compound
Sentences

► **Rewrite the letter. Use each pair of sentences to write
a compound sentence. Use joining words and commas
correctly. Sign your name.**

Dear Officer Buckle,
(1) I liked your talk. My friends also liked it. (2) We knew some safety rules. You taught us many new ones. (3) We remember most of your safety rules. We forgot a few. (4) May we send you questions? Will you send us answers? (5) Please come back. Don't forget to bring Gloria!
Sincerely,

Dear Officer Buckle, _____

_____

_____

_____

_____

_____

_____

_____

► **Check your new letter. Have you used commas correctly?**

Name_____

▶ If a word group is a sentence, write *complete sentence*. If it is not a sentence, rewrite it to make it a complete sentence.

1. Officer Buckle.

_____

2. Officer Buckle and Gloria gave their talk together.

_____

3. Got bored and began to yawn.

_____

▶ Read each sentence. Then write *compound subject* or *compound predicate* on the line that follows it.

4. Cal and I went to the talk. _____

5. We laughed and cheered. _____

6. Officer Buckle and Gloria were great! _____

▶ Join the two sentences to make a compound sentence. Use the word in parentheses ( ).

7. Gloria is just a dog. She is smarter than most dogs. **(but)**

_____

_____

8. Officer Buckle teaches safety. He wants children to stay safe. **(and)**

_____

_____

Compound Subjects and Predicates;
Compound Sentences

Harcourt

Skill Reminder

- A **common noun** names any person, animal, place, or thing.
- A **proper noun** names a particular person, animal, place, or thing.
- Each important word of a proper noun begins with a capital letter.

▶ Circle the common and proper nouns in each sentence.

1. Yuko swept the sand.

2. The turtle came out of the Pacific Ocean.

3. Her eggs had leathery shells.

4. Taro enjoyed being with his old friend.

5. Jiro-San knew about the ocean.

▶ For each common noun, write a proper noun. For each proper noun, write a common noun.

COMMON	PROPER
6. teacher	_____
7. _____	California
8. cat	_____
9. _____	Monday
10. building	_____

Harcourt

▶ **Read the story below. Write
each noun from the story in the
correct place in the chart to tell
whether it names a person, an
animal, a place, or a thing. If it
is a proper noun, write _P_ after
it in the chart.**

Taro lived in Japan, in a house near the Pacific Ocean.
One Sunday in September, he went to visit his friend.
Jiro-San used a broom to sweep the sand and make the
beach safe. Later, the boy saw a turtle in Uchiuro Bay. He
named it Trixie.

PERSON	PLACE

ANIMAL	THING

Harcourt

Name _____

▶ **Write either *compound subject, compound predicate,* or *compound sentence* to describe each sentence.**

1. The brother and sister walked quickly. _____

2. The children were late, and the old man was waiting.

   _____

3. One turtle came out of the sea and laid some eggs.

   _____

4. Taro, Yuko, and Jiro-San watched. _____

5. The eggs hatched in September, and the beach was full of

   baby turtles. _____

▶ **Circle the nouns in each sentence. Write *C* above common nouns and *P* above proper nouns. Then rewrite each sentence, using capital letters to start proper nouns.**

6. The children live in japan.

   _____

7. Uchiuro bay is on the pacific ocean.

   _____

8. Some children thought jiro-san was strange, but taro liked him.

   _____

   _____

Harcourt

Name _____

Skill Reminder

• A **singular noun** names one person, animal, place, or thing.
  A **plural noun** names more than one person, animal, place,
  or thing.
• Add *s* or *es* to make most nouns plural. For nouns that end in a
  consonant and *y*, change *y* to *i* and add *es*.

▶ Circle the nouns. Write *S* above each singular noun. Write *P* above
each plural noun.

1. Please put these photographs in the album.

2. Where is the picture of the four hawks?

3. Their wings are as wide as our car.

4. Those birds live high in the mountains.

5. Always bring your camera on trips.

▶ Write the plural form of each singular noun. Write the singular form
of each plural noun.

6. eagle _____

7. _____ holidays

8. hill _____

9. _____ kisses

10. berry _____

11. _____ bunnies

12. guppy _____

13. _____ branches

14. wish _____

15. _____ matches

Harcourt

Singular and Plural Nouns

Name _____

▶ **Write the plural form of the noun in parentheses ( )
to complete each sentence.**

1. Three _____ were on the beach. **(turtle)**

2. They laid their _____ on the wet sand. **(egg)**

3. Four _____ flew overhead. **(seagull)**

4. Some _____ were on one turtle. **(fly)**

5. There are many _____ on this island. **(beach)**

▶ **Rewrite each sentence, using the plural form of the underlined noun.
Each new sentence is started for you.**

6. The <u>canary</u> flew into the tree.

    Two _____

7. A <u>spider</u> crawled on the leaf.

    A few _____

8. One <u>branch</u> fell during a storm.

    Three _____

Harcourt

Singular and Plural Nouns

Name_____

▶ **Rewrite these sentences. Write proper nouns correctly, and add the correct end mark.**

1. Aunt rita took me to a zoo

_____

2. The zoo is in chicago

_____

3. What an exciting trip that was

_____

4. Has pablo seen the penguins

_____

5. Come with us next time

_____

▶ **Circle the nouns. Write *S* above the singular nouns. Write *P* above the plural nouns. For each singular noun, write the plural form on the line to the right.**

6. Some rabbits were near the bush. _____

7. The birds sat on their perch. _____

8. Our cousins have arrived from the city. _____

9. My parents cook our meal. _____

10. Our friends fill the day with activities. _____

Statements and Questions;
Commands and Exclamations;
Common and Proper Nouns;
Singular and Plural Nouns

Harcourt

Skill Reminder

- Some nouns change their spelling in the plural form.
- Some nouns have the same spelling for both the singular and plural forms.

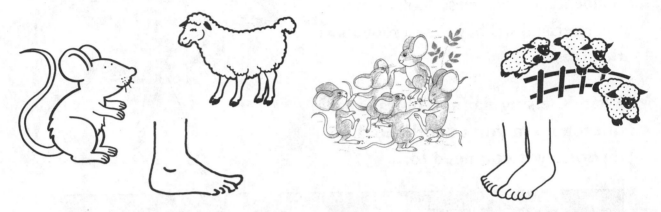

▶ Complete this chart of singular and plural nouns. Use a dictionary if you need to.

SINGULAR	PLURAL
1. woman	
2. mouse	
3.	geese

SINGULAR	PLURAL
4. foot	
5.	teeth
6. child	

▶ Complete this chart of singular and plural nouns.

SINGULAR	PLURAL
7. deer	
8. moose	

SINGULAR	PLURAL
9. trout	
10.	sheep

Harcourt

▶ **1.–5. Read this paragraph. Underline five irregular nouns.**

The men and women traveled toward a river. There they saw a lonely moose. Suddenly, twelve geese took off from the riverbanks. They flew a foot above the trees.

▶ **Write the singular and plural forms of each noun you underlined. Use a dictionary if you need to.**

SINGULAR	PLURAL
6.	
7.	
8.	
9.	
10.	

Harcourt

Name _____

▶ **Circle the nouns. Write *C* above common nouns and *P* above proper nouns. Then rewrite the proper nouns correctly.**

1. I got a letter on tuesday. _____

2. It was from alaska. _____

3. My uncle lives in nome. _____

4. Bill, my cousin, sent me a picture. _____

5. It showed a statue of balto. _____

▶ **Write the correct plural form of each singular noun. Use a dictionary if you need to.**

6. man _____
7. child _____
8. city _____

9. horse _____
10. tooth _____
11. baby _____
12. doctor _____
13. building _____

14. deer _____
15. couch _____

Common and Proper Nouns;
Singular and Plural Nouns;
More Plural Nouns

Name_____

Skill Reminder

- **A possessive noun** tells who or what something belongs to.
- **A singular possessive noun** shows ownership by one person or thing. Add an apostrophe (') and an *s* to a singular noun to show ownership.

▶ **Circle the possessive noun in each sentence.**

1. We saw George's eggs in the nest.

2. The dinosaur's name should be Georgina.

3. The mother's eggs will become baby dinosaurs.

▶ **Write the possessive form of the noun in parentheses ( ).**

4. _____ story is a fairy tale. **(Mr. dePaola)**

5. The _____ characters are cave dwellers. **(story)**

6. The _____ story is not real. **(author)**

7. A dinosaur could never be a _____ pet. **(boy)**

▶ **Choose three nouns from the box. Write three sentences, using the possessive form of the nouns you choose.**

woman	baby	writer	student	teacher

8. _____

9. _____

10. _____

Harcourt

Name_____

▶ **Follow the directions to change each singular noun into a singular possessive noun.**

1. animal + apostrophe + *s* = _____

2. boy + apostrophe + *s* = _____

3. cave dweller + apostrophe + *s* = _____

4. aunt + apostrophe + *s* = _____

5. chief + apostrophe + *s* = _____

6. mother + apostrophe + *s* = _____

▶ **Write a sentence for each pair of nouns. Use the possessive form of the first noun to show ownership of the second noun. An example is done for you.**

    Example: train   tracks

       The train's tracks were being fixed.

7. caveman   club

_____

8. dinosaur   egg

_____

9. baby   toy

_____

10. artist   picture

_____

Singular Possessive Nouns

Name_____

▶ **Read the passage and choose the word that belongs in each space. Fill in the circle for the correct answer.**

Was George a good pet? He ate all the leaves off all the __(1)__ . The __(2)__ cave was lit with eight __(3)__ . When George sneezed, it was a disaster.

George had four very big __(4)__ . All of __(5)__ pots were broken. Later on, George laid some eggs. What would __(6)__ __(7)__ look like?

Perhaps Little Grunt should have had a __(8)__ for a pet.

1 ⬭ bushs
⬭ bushes
⬭ bushies
⬭ bush's

2 ⬭ tribe
⬭ tribes
⬭ tribe's
⬭ tribies

3 ⬭ torches
⬭ torche's
⬭ torchs
⬭ torch

4 ⬭ foot
⬭ feet
⬭ foots
⬭ feets

5 ⬭ Mama
⬭ Mamas'
⬭ Mama's
⬭ Mamas

6 ⬭ Georges
⬭ George's
⬭ Georges'
⬭ Georg's

7 ⬭ baby
⬭ babys
⬭ babyes
⬭ babies

8 ⬭ sheep
⬭ sheeps
⬭ sheep's
⬭ sheepes

Harcourt

Singular and Plural Nouns;
Singular Possessive Nouns

Theme 2 Review

▶ **Join the two sentences to make a compound sentence. Write the compound sentence correctly on the lines.**

1. Officer Buckle teaches safety. That dog is his partner. **(and)**

_____

_____

2. His talks were good. Gloria made them even better. **(but)**

_____

_____

▶ **Circle the nouns. Write *C* above common nouns. Write *P* above proper nouns.**

3. Taro and the old man sailed out to sea.

4. Jiro-San knew many secrets.

5. He knew the turtles would come in July.

6. Eight weeks later, the eggs hatched.

▶ **Write the correct plural form of each singular noun.**

7. torch _____

8. monkey _____

9. month _____

10. puppy _____

11. penguin _____

12. canary _____

13. bush _____

14. cave _____

GO ON

Harcourt

Name _____

Theme 2 Review

▶ Complete this chart of singular and plural nouns. Use a dictionary if you need to.

SINGULAR	PLURAL
15. tooth	
16.	deer
17. child	

SINGULAR	PLURAL
18. woman	
19. foot	
20.	mice

▶ Write the possessive form of the noun in parentheses ( ).

21. _____ pancakes were good. **(Mama)**

22. The _____ teddy bear is cute. **(baby)**

23. _____ pet is getting bigger. **(Little Grunt)**

24. The _____ cave is too small. **(tribe)**

25. When did _____ eggs hatch? **(George)**

Theme 2 Review

Name_____

- **A plural possessive noun** shows ownership by more than one person or thing.
- **To show ownership, add only an apostrophe (') to a plural noun that ends in s.**

▶ **Circle the possessive noun in each sentence.**

1. These kites' tails are made of rags.

2. People admire the kids' kites.

3. My parents' newspapers made a good kite.

4. Can you see those boys' kites up there?

5. The kites are as colorful as those birds' wings.

▶ **Write the possessive form of the plural noun in parentheses ( ) to complete each sentence.**

6. The _____ house is next door. (**DeWettes**)

7. The _____ car is in the driveway. (**grown-ups**)

8. Their _____ bicycles are nearby. (**sons**)

9. The _____ toys are scattered. (**boys**)

10. Julian plays with his _____ toys. (**friends**)

▶ **Choose two plural nouns from the box below. Write two sentences. Use the plural possessive form of each noun you choose.**

boys	girls	adults	playmates	robins

11. _____

12. _____

Harcourt

Name _____

▶ **Write the plural form of each noun. Then write the plural possessive form.**

SINGULAR	PLURAL	PLURAL POSSESSIVE
1. playmate		
2. schoolgirl		
3. mother		
4. family		
5. brother		

▶ **Use each plural possessive noun you wrote above in a sentence of your own.**

6. _____

_____

7. _____

_____

8. _____

_____

9. _____

_____

10. _____

_____

Plural Possessive Nouns

Harcourt

Name _____

▶ **Complete the chart with the correct form of each noun.**

SINGULAR	PLURAL	SINGULAR POSSESSIVE	PLURAL POSSESSIVE
1. lion			
2. thrush			
3. giraffe			
4. butterfly			
5. fox			

▶ **Write the correct singular or plural possessive form of the noun in parentheses ( ).**

6. The _____ hours are 8:00 A.M. to 6:00 P.M. **(zoo)**

7. Gloria admires the _____ playground. **(monkeys)**

8. Where is the _____ pen? **(bears)**

9. Look at the baby _____ toy. **(gorilla)**

10. Julian is amazed at the _____ size. **(elephants)**

Singular and Plural Nouns
Possessive Nouns; Plural Possessive Nouns

GRAMMAR PRACTICE BOOK **43**

Harcourt

Name _____

2

3

Skill Reminder

- An **abbreviation** is a short way to write a word. Use a period after most abbreviations.
- Begin abbreviations for proper nouns with capital letters.

▶ Draw lines to match each word with its abbreviation.

1. Monday   Mar.
2. March   Feb.
3. Mister   Fri.
4. Friday   Mon.
5. February   Mr.

"Come to Mr. Bibb's class's talent show on Friday, March 3. Please respond by Monday, February 27."

▶ Rewrite the abbreviations correctly.

6. mr Jay _____
7. ms Grey _____
8. oct 19 _____
9. mrs Pitt _____
10. Oak rd _____
11. aug 9 _____
12. thurs _____
13. Loon ave _____
14. wed _____
15. dr Sanchez _____

▶ Find the words in this sentence that could be abbreviated. Write the abbreviations on the line below.

16.–20. On Tuesday, April 3, Mister Lunez is taking our class to the museum on Danby Avenue to see artworks about United States history.

_____

Harcourt

Name _____

▶ **Help Beany organize her address book alphabetically.**
Use the last names to help you. Write the people's names, addresses,
and birthdays on the pages where they belong. Use abbreviations for
titles, streets, and months.

Mister George Adams
15 Myrtle Avenue
September 5

Mister John Creasy
624 Beach Road
August 3

Doctor Rita Arnez
72 Pleasant Street
October 30

Mistress Ann Coe
798 Pilgrim Road
December 18

Mistress Gertie Boyle
3221 Holly Avenue
February 20

Mister Myron Bates
320 Lombard Street
March 1

▶ **Rewrite these sentences. Begin and end them correctly.**

1. our playground has new swings

   _____

2. two of them are tire swings

   _____

3. each one can hold two people

   _____

4. my friend Carol Ann swings with me

   _____

5. leo pushes us higher and higher

   _____

▶ **Rewrite these plural possessive nouns and abbreviations correctly.**

6. boys gym _____   11. dec 4 _____

7. dr fry _____   12. girls team _____

8. sept 10 _____   13. ladies room _____

9. sky st _____   14. thurs _____

10. mister otis _____   15. ms Babbitt _____

Sentences; Capitalization
Plural Possessive Nouns
Abbreviations

Skill Reminder

> • **A singular pronoun** takes the place of a singular noun. **Always capitalize the pronoun** *I*.
> SINGULAR PRONOUNS: I, me, you, he, she, him, her, it
> • **A plural pronoun** takes the place of a plural noun.
> PLURAL PRONOUNS: we, us, you, they, them

▶ **Underline the two pronouns in each sentence.**

1. I told you about the class for Visiting Dogs.

2. We first watched it last September.

3. You can join us at the next class.

4. He and she are the teachers.

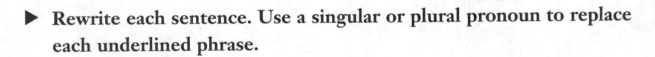

Visiting Dogs

5. I will ask them where to meet.

▶ **Rewrite each sentence. Use a singular or plural pronoun to replace each underlined phrase.**

6. That boy wants a visitor.

   _____

7. Ask those dog owners for their ideas.

   _____

8. Show the walker to that dog.

   _____

▶ **Find the two phrases in this sentence that could be changed to pronouns. Write the new sentence.**

9.–10. The dogs learned the rules right away.

   _____

Harcourt

► **People in the hospital enjoy receiving visitors. Read
this thank-you note. The writer has repeated many nouns. Rewrite
the body of the thank-you note, using one pronoun to replace each
underlined word or phrase. Underline the pronouns you used.**

Dear Rosie,
    <u>Lisa</u> would like to thank <u>Rosie</u> for visiting
last week. <u>Lisa</u> really enjoyed the visit.
<u>The visit</u> cheered <u>Lisa</u> up!
    Sometimes the hospital is fun, but often
<u>the hospital</u> is dull. The nurses try hard.
However, <u>the nurses</u> have too much to do.
Visitors are important. <u>Lisa and the other</u>
<u>patients</u> all look forward to <u>visitors</u>.
Please come to visit <u>Lisa and the other</u>
<u>patients</u> again.
                    Your Friend,
                        Lisa

1.–10.

_____

_____

_____

_____

_____

Name _____

▶ **Rewrite these abbreviations correctly.**

1. dr Deeds _____

2. ms Sands _____

3. aug 4 _____

4. jan 15 _____

5. River rd _____

6. oct 31 _____

7. mon _____

8. Elm st _____

9. mar 10 _____

10. mrs luz _____

▶ **Rewrite each sentence. Use a singular or plural pronoun to replace each underlined phrase.**

11. The mice ran around the cage.

_____

12. The mouse ran around the cage.

_____

13. The mouse looked at the child.

_____

14. The mouse looked at the children.

_____

Harcourt

Skill Reminder

• **A subject pronoun** takes the place of one or more nouns in the subject of a sentence.
   SUBJECT PRONOUNS: I, you, he, she, it, we, they
• Always capitalize the pronoun *I*.

▶ **Underline the subject pronoun in each sentence.**

1. She always hits home runs.

2. Today we will see José play.

3. He catches fly balls.

4. They fly far overhead.

5. I respect José's talent.

▶ **Rewrite each sentence. Use a subject pronoun to replace the underlined word(s).**

6. José caught a high fly ball.

7. His father and I clapped wildly.

   _____

8. His teammates tossed their caps in the air.

   _____

▶ **Rewrite these sentences correctly. Capitalize the pronoun *I*.**

9. Carmen and i practice hitting.

   _____

10. i and she are pretty good.

Harcourt

▶ José wrote to a friend to tell him about playing baseball. Help José finish his letter. Add the correct subject pronouns from the box.

I	You	He	We	They

Dear Sam,

(1) ___ really like our new coach, Mr. Deebs. (2) _____ works us very hard. (3) _____ would be so tired after one of our practices!

Carmen and her teammates are doing well. (4) _____ might win the pennant. (5) _____ are both lucky to have a father who loves baseball.

Your friend,
José

▶ Now use the subject pronouns from the box above in sentences of your own.

6. _____

7. _____

8. _____

9. _____

10. _____

Harcourt

▶ **In sentences 1–5, draw one line under the complete subject. Draw two lines under the complete predicate.**

1. The players practice every day.

2. Coach Lane teaches them.

3. Our team does well in the playoffs.

4. We finish third overall.

5. It pleases our parents and our coach.

▶ **Rewrite each sentence. Use a subject pronoun to replace the underlined word(s). Then write _S_ if the subject is singular or _P_ if the subject is plural.**

6. The pitchers are warming up.

   _____

7. Carmen and I take practice swings.

   _____

8. Mr. Mendez watches from the stands.

   _____

9. The pitcher's mound seems far away.

   _____

10. Carmen is the most valuable player.

    _____

Subjects and Predicates
Singular and Plural Pronouns; Subject Pronouns

Harcourt

Skill Reminder

> • An **object pronoun** follows an action verb or a word such as *about, at, for, from, near, of, to,* or *with.*
> **OBJECT PRONOUNS:** me, you, him, her, it, us, them
> • Use *I* and *me* last with other nouns and pronouns.

▶ **Underline the object pronoun in each sentence.**

1. Ramona hugs her gently.

2. That baby is fond of you.

3. Father carries the baby with him.

4. Mother shows us the baby gifts.

5. Beezus puts them upstairs.

▶ **Rewrite each sentence. Use an object pronoun to replace each underlined phrase.**

6. Roberta dropped <u>the rattle</u>.

_____

7. Ramona poured tea for <u>the dolls</u>.

_____

8. Beezus tossed the ball to <u>Ramona and me</u>.

_____

_____

▶ **Rewrite these sentences correctly.**

9. Give the bottles to me and Ramona.

_____

10. The baby smiled at Beezus and I.

_____

Harcourt

► Write the correct object pronoun from the box below
to replace the underlined words.

them	her	it	him	us

1. I threw the ball to <u>the tallest boy</u>. _____

2. Beezus likes to play with <u>our baby sister</u>. _____

3. I told my class at school about <u>Beezus and the baby</u>. _____

4. They made a card for <u>my family and me</u>. _____

5. Daddy taped <u>the card</u> to the refrigerator. _____

► Ramona wrote about her new sister. Rewrite her sentences correctly.

I can't wait to play with she.

Will she share a room with I?

Beezus will beat me and her at games.

6. _____

7. _____

8. _____

▶ **Choose the best way to write each underlined section, and fill in the bubble for the correct answer. If the underlined section needs no change, mark the choice "No mistake."**

(1) <u>Ramona and me are friends.</u> She has a new little sister. The two girls

share a **(2)** <u>room, and it gets along well.</u> The older sister is named

Beezus. **(3)** <u>She goes to a different school.</u> **(4)** <u>Her and my sister</u> are

in a club together.

1 ◯ Ramona and I are friends.

◯ I and Ramona are friends.

◯ Ramona and i are friends.

◯ No mistake

2 ◯ room, it gets along well.

◯ room gets along well.

◯ room, and they get along well.

◯ No mistake

3 ◯ It goes to a different school.

◯ He goes to a different school.

◯ A different school she goes.

◯ No mistake

4 ◯ My sister and her

◯ My sister and he

◯ She and my sister

◯ No mistake

Harcourt

Name_____

Theme 3 Review

Plural Possessive Nouns
Abbreviations
Singular and Plural
Pronouns
Subject Pronouns
Object Pronouns

▶ Write the plural form of each noun. Then write the plural possessive form.

SINGULAR	PLURAL	PLURAL POSSESSIVE
1. teacher		
2. pal		
3. puppy		
4. grandmother		
5. uncle		

▶ Rewrite the abbreviations correctly.

6. dr Ives   _____

7. ms Neal   _____

8. nov 1   _____

9. sat   _____

10. Rye st   _____

11. apr 10   _____

12. thurs   _____

13. New ave   _____

14. mr. Ryan   _____

15. mrs Chin   _____

▶ Rewrite each sentence. Use a singular or plural pronoun to replace the underlined word or words.

16. <u>Rosa</u> is new in school.

_____

17. Keri introduced <u>the girl</u> to our class.

_____

Harcourt

Theme 3 Review

18. The <u>boys</u> made room for Rosa.

_____

19. Rosa put a <u>book</u> on her desk.

_____

20. Could you move <u>those books</u>?

_____

▶ **Draw one line under each subject pronoun. Draw two lines under each object pronoun.**

21. She met me at the door.

22. I gave them a big hug.

23. You know her from art class.

▶ **Rewrite each sentence correctly.**

24. Me and Sarah walk to school together.

_____

25. The teacher gave me and Pablo a project to do.

_____

Harcourt

Skill Reminder

An **adjective** is a word that describes a noun. An adjective can come before the noun it describes. An adjective can follow a verb such as *is* or *seems*.

▶ **Circle the adjective that describes each underlined noun.**

1. The <u>desert</u> is dry.

2. Many <u>animals</u> live there.

3. A <u>cactus</u> is thorny.

4. We saw a red <u>flower</u>.

5. Little <u>water</u> reaches the plants.

▶ **Circle each adjective. Underline the noun it describes.**

6. The sly coyote had a bow.

7. He built a huge ladder.

8. The ladder reached the faraway sky.

9. Coyote climbed for many days.

10. On the cool moon, he rested.

▶ **These sentences include adjectives that come before a noun. Circle each adjective and underline each noun it describes. Then rewrite each sentence so that the adjective comes after the noun. An example has been done for you.**

That is a (mysterious) <u>owl</u>. → That <u>owl</u> is (mysterious).

11. Those are bright stars. _____

12. This is wonderful artwork. _____

Harcourt

Name _____

▶ **Read the story about Coyote. Circle ten adjectives.**
Underline the nouns they describe.

1.–10. Coyote woke on a cold morning. He met big Bear and tiny

Roadrunner near the river.

"We are going to race," said Bear. "Who will win? Make a guess."

Coyote thought for a long minute. Bear was strong. Roadrunner was

fast. "I choose Roadrunner," he said.

Away they ran. Suddenly Bear stepped on a sharp stone. Then

Roadrunner tripped over a spiny cactus. The runners were sad.

"Cheer up," said Coyote. "Both of you win, and you can still be

best friends."

▶ **Use each adjective in the box to write a sentence about Coyote.**

clever	happy	noisy	proud

11. _____

_____

12. _____

_____

13. _____

_____

14. _____

_____

Adjectives

Harcourt

▶ **Underline the correct pronoun of the two in parentheses ( ).**

1. **(We, Us)** like the view of the desert.

2. The hotel manager is speaking to **(I, me)**.

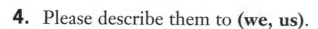

3. **(She, Her)** warns us about the coyotes.

4. Please describe them to **(we, us)**.

5. **(I, Me)** heard a coyote last night.

▶ **Think of an adjective to describe each underlined noun. Rewrite the sentence, adding the adjective.**

6. I admire the <u>cactus</u>.

_____

7. What a <u>view</u> this is!

_____

8. A <u>lizard</u> basks in the sun.

_____

9. Our <u>car</u> is parked outside.

_____

10. The <u>sign</u> blinks off and on.

_____

Harcourt

Subject and Object Pronouns
Adjectives

Name _____

Skill Reminder

Some adjectives tell what kind. Adjectives can describe size, shape, or color. Adjectives can describe how something looks, sounds, feels, tastes, or smells.

▶ Circle the adjective that tells what kind.

1. The owl woke the bright sun.

2. Monkey killed a little owlet.

3. Now the night is long.

4. The sad owl will not hoot.

▶ Rewrite the sentence three times. Add adjectives that answer the questions in parentheses ( ).

The owl flew away.

5. _____ (what size?)

6. _____ (what shape?)

7. _____ (what color?)

▶ Complete the chart with adjectives that tell what kind.

SIGHT	SOUND	TOUCH	TASTE	SMELL
8.	9.	10.	11.	12.

Harcourt

Adjectives for *What Kind*

Name_____

▶ **Look at the pictures. Place each adjective in the correct column.**

| tiny | curved | black | spotted | slender |
| long | large | pointed | patterned | |

	SIZE	SHAPE	COLOR
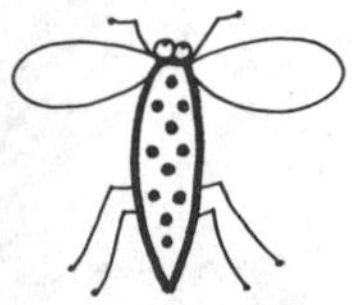	1.	4.	7.
	2.	5.	8.
	3.	6.	9.

▶ **Choose one picture from those above. Write three sentences that describe it. Use the adjectives you wrote in the boxes.**

10. _____

11. _____

12. _____

Adjectives for *What Kind*

Harcourt

Name _____

▶ **Circle the adjective in each sentence. Underline the noun it describes.**

1. We visited a great zoo.

2. I liked the funny monkeys.

3. A bouncy seal barked at me.

4. I bought a red balloon.

5. The huge lion scared me.

▶ **Underline the nouns in each sentence. Then rewrite the sentence, adding an adjective that describes one of the nouns.**

6. A hippo shared its pen with a bird.

   _____

7. Students found the path to the giraffes.

   _____

8. Mr. Evans showed Mary the bears.

   _____

9. Penguins dove into the pond for fish.

   _____

10. A seal splashed Juan with its tail.

   _____

Common and Proper Nouns
Adjectives for *What Kind*

Skill Reminder

Some adjectives tell how many. Not all adjectives that tell
how many give an exact number.

▶ **Circle the adjective that tells how many.**

1. Verna sent her book to three publishers.

2. She revised the book five times.

3. The book will be seventy-five pages long.

4. Forty bookstore chains will sell it.

5. It will be translated into ten languages.

▶ **Rewrite sentences 1.–5. Replace the number words with adjectives
that tell how many without giving an exact number.**

6. _____

7. _____

8. _____

9. _____

10. _____

▶ **Write two sentences about your own writing. Use adjectives that tell
how many.**

11. _____

12. _____

Harcourt

Name _____

▶ **Here is a picture about one of Verna Aardema's folktales. The sentences below describe what you see. Circle the adjectives that tell how many.**

1. The picture shows ten lambs in a field.

2. Several reeds fill the end of the pond.

3. You can see two ducks swimming.

4. Some hills are in the distance.

5. One wolf is watching.

▶ **Draw your own picture here. Then write sentences to describe it. Use adjectives that tell how many.**

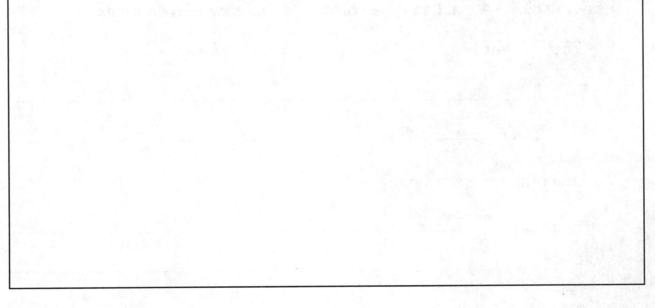

6. _____

7. _____

8. _____

Harcourt

Adjectives for *How Many*

▶ **Circle the adjective in each sentence. Underline the noun it describes.**

1. The swamp was hot.

2. I saw a big alligator.

3. A pink flamingo flew by.

4. It rested on one leg.

5. Many bugs pestered us.

▶ **Rewrite each sentence two times. The first time, add an adjective that tells what kind. The second time, add an adjective that tells how many. An example has been done for you.**

I saw birds. → **a. I saw red birds.**   **b. I saw eleven birds.**

6. They caught fish.

   a. _____

   b. _____

7. Dragonflies flew around.

   a. _____

   b. _____

8. Raindrops fell.

   a. _____

   b. _____

Adjectives for *What Kind*
Adjectives for *How Many*

Harcourt

Name _____

Skill Reminder

The adjectives *a, an,* and *the* are called **articles.** Use *a* and *an* for singular nouns. Use *the* for both singular and plural nouns. Use *a* before a word that begins with a consonant sound. Use *an* before a word that begins with a vowel sound.

▶ **Circle the article in each sentence. Underline the noun it introduces.**

1. We buy food at a grocery.

2. In Chewandswallow, food falls from the sky.

3. The story is very silly.

4. Imagine an egg falling into your plate.

5. Could you eat a pizza at every meal?

▶ **Complete each sentence with *a* or *an*.**

6. Please hand me ___ fork.

7. I am trying to eat ___ eggplant.

8. It fell out of ___ cloud.

9. I would rather have ___ ice-cream cone.

▶ **Write three sentences about food. Use the article in parentheses ( ) in your sentence.**

10. _____ (a)

11. _____ (an)

12. _____ (the)

Harcourt

▶ Here is a news story about a storm in Chewandswallow.
Complete the story by adding the articles *a*, *an*, or *the* where
they are needed.

Chewandswallow
Spaghetti & Meatball Storm

CHEWANDSWALLOW **(1)** _____ storm hit this small town on

Wednesday night. **(2)** _____ storm lasted for about **(3)** _____ hour.

(4) _____ car driving down **(5)** _____ main street was blown away. Luckily,

(6) _____ passengers were rescued.

Oddly, **(7)** _____ rain from this storm fell in **(8)** _____ form of

spaghetti and meatballs. **(9)** _____ noodles wrapped themselves around

buildings. They made **(10)** _____ mess. **(11)** _____ bulldozer was needed

to remove **(12)** _____ meatballs.

(13) _____ mayor was out of town, but twelve aldermen helped clean

up. One alderman said, "This is **(14)** _____ emergency. What we really

need is **(15)** _____ army with forks and knives!"

Harcourt

Name _____

▶ **Complete each sentence by adding an adjective that answers the question in parentheses ( ).**

1. We visited a _____ farm. **(What size?)**

2. I saw _____ piglets. **(How many?)**

3. The farm had a _____ barn. **(What color?)**

4. We ate some _____ apples. **(How did they taste?)**

5. We fed _____ chickens. **(How many?)**

6. I rode a _____ pony. **(What color?)**

7. He ate _____ carrots. **(How many?)**

8. The ducks made a _____ noise. **(How did they sound?)**

▶ **Underline the correct article in parentheses ( ).**

9. I wish I lived on **(a, an)** farm.

10. **(An, The)** animals are so wonderful!

11. Farmer Greely must be **(a, an)** early riser.

12. His children feed **(a, the)** goats.

Harcourt

Adjectives
Articles

Skill Reminder

Adjectives can describe by comparing people, animals, places, or
things. Use either *-er* or *more* with adjectives to compare two
things. Use either *-est* or *most* with adjectives to compare more
than two things.

▶ **Circle the adjective that compares. Underline the words that tell
which people or things are being compared.**

1. Molly is taller than her brother.

2. Meg is the quietest of the children in her family.

3. This house is more crowded than a stable.

▶ **Underline the correct form of the two adjectives
in parentheses ( ).**

4. Was the donkey **(louder, loudest)** than the goat?

5. He was the **(stronger, strongest)** animal in the barn.

6. He was **(more active, most active)** than the chickens.

▶ **Complete each sentence with the correct form of the adjective
in parentheses ( ).**

7. Bartholemew was _____ than anyone
   else. **(intelligent)**

8. The house seemed _____ than it had
   before. **(calm)**

9. Mother was the _____ of all. **(relaxed)**

10. The house seemed _____ without the
    animals. **(large)**

Harcourt

Name _____

▶ **Complete this chart with adjectives that compare.**

ADJECTIVE	COMPARING TWO THINGS	COMPARING MORE THAN TWO THINGS
1. loud	louder	
2. crowded		most crowded
3. difficult		
4. small		
5. unpleasant		

▶ **Use some of the words you wrote above to write five sentences about John the Carpenter's home. This picture may give you ideas.**

6. _____

7. _____

8. _____

9. _____

10. _____

Adjectives That Compare

Name _____

▶ **Choose the best way to write each underlined section and fill in the bubble for the correct answer. If the underlined section needs no change, mark the choice *No mistake*.**

(1) Molly is the older one of the four girls. She has three sisters and four

brothers. They live **(2)** with their parents in an house that is very crowded.

(3) It is the most frenzied household you have ever seen. **(4)** Even an

animals live in the house.

1 ⬭ Molly is the oldest one of the four girls.

⬭ Molly is the most old one of the four girls.

⬭ Molly is the most oldest one of the four girls.

⬭ No mistake

2 ⬭ in an house with their parents

⬭ with their parents in a house

⬭ with their parents in the house

⬭ No mistake

3 ⬭ It is the frenziedest household

⬭ It is a most frenzied household

⬭ It is the frenzied household

⬭ No mistake

4 ⬭ Even a animals live in the house.

⬭ Even an animal live in the house.

⬭ Even the animals live in the house.

⬭ No mistake

Articles
Adjectives That Compare

Harcourt

Name _____

Theme 4 Review

Adjectives
Adjectives for
What Kind
Adjectives for
How Many
Articles
Adjectives That Compare

▶ **Circle the adjective in each sentence. Underline the noun it describes.**

1. She told us a wonderful story.

2. It was about a beautiful princess.

3. A terrible dragon threatened her.

4. She scared it with a green wand.

5. The dragon vanished with a great bang.

6. Then the princess was happy.

▶ **Write the adjective from each sentence in the chart where it belongs.**

7. I checked out five books.

8. I like the book with the square cover.

9. It has pictures of giant trucks.

10. The truck on the cover is purple.

11. It can carry fifty tons.

12. Read me some stories, please.

WHAT KIND	HOW MANY

Name _____

Theme 4 Review

▶ **Rewrite each sentence, filling in the blank with *a* or *an*.**

13. I read _____ article about the ocean.

_____

14. It was written by _____ author from Peru.

_____

15. She is _____ scientist who studies ocean life.

_____

16. A scientist of that kind is called _____ oceanographer.

_____

17. She has written _____ book for children.

_____

▶ **Complete each sentence with the correct form of the adjective in parentheses ( ).**

18. This story is _____ than that one. **(thrilling)**

19. I am a _____ reader than you are. **(slow)**

20. Mark reads the _____ of all. **(fast)**

▶ **Write two sentences. Use forms of *small* to compare two things and to compare more than two things.**

21. _____

22. _____

Name _____

Skill Reminder

> • The **verb** is the main word in the predicate of a sentence.
> • An **action verb** tells what the subject of a sentence does.

▶ Circle the action verb in each sentence.

1. The sun shone brightly.

2. No rain fell on the ground.

3. The corn died in the fields.

4. The farmers watched the sky.

5. Most of the crop failed.

6. Some families moved away.

7. Everyone hoped for better days.

▶ Rewrite each sentence, filling in the blank with an action verb.

8. The farmers _____ hard in their fields.

_____

_____

9. Grasshoppers _____ many of the leaves.

_____

_____

10. The wind _____ dust all around the farm.

_____

_____

Harcourt

Action Verbs

Name _____

▶ **Fill in the blank with an action verb.**

1. Leah _____ fresh coffee cake.

2. Papa _____ the pigs and some of the cattle.

3. Mama _____ dishwater on her petunias.

4. Leah _____ her pony.

▶ **Find the action verb in each sentence, and write it on the line.**

5. The neighbors said good-bye. _____

6. Papa borrowed money from the bank. _____

7. Leah clutched her dollar. _____

8. She wanted to save the farm. _____

▶ **Choose two verbs from the box. Use each verb you choose in a sentence of your own.**

dried	ruined	planted	saved

9. _____

   _____

10. _____

   _____

Harcourt

▶ **Write the correct form of the adjective in parentheses ( ).**

1. Leah had the _____ pony of all. **(wonderful)**

2. It had a _____ coat than any other pony. **(nice)**

3. Mr. B. shouted, "That's the _____ pony in the county." **(fine)**

4. This year is _____ than last year. **(difficult)**

▶ **Rewrite each sentence. Begin and end each sentence correctly. Begin proper nouns with capital letters.**

5. what an amazing auction we had in july

   _____

   _____

6. did the man in the big hat come from chicago

   _____

   _____

7. the family eats coffee cake every saturday

   _____

   _____

▶ **Draw two lines under the predicate of each sentence. Then circle the action verb.**

8. The Great Depression began in 1929.

9. It lasted for ten years.

10. The price of farm products fell.

Adjectives That Compare
Common and Proper Nouns; Action Verbs

Harcourt

• A **helping verb** works with the **main verb** to tell about an action.
• The words *have, has,* and *had* are often used as helping verbs.

▶ **Underline the main verb. Circle the helping verb.**

1. The coyote is dreaming of a javelina dinner.

2. The javelinas could ignore the danger.

3. The coyote has chased two javelinas.

4. Their little houses have collapsed.

5. The coyote was destroying them.

▶ **Complete each sentence with *have* or *has*.**

6. The coyote _____ called to the javelinas.

7. The clever javelinas _____ not answered.

8. Now their enemy _____ used his magic.

▶ **Use the verb shown and *have, has,* or *had* in a sentence of your own.**

9. frightened

_____

_____

10. howled

_____

_____

Harcourt

Main and Helping Verbs

▶ **Put the story sentences in order. Underline the main verbs and circle the helping verbs.**

Three javelinas have moved to the desert.

The javelinas have trapped him in a stove.

At the third house, he has cornered all three

javelinas. They have designed three houses.

A mean coyote has visited each house.

1. _____

2. _____

3. _____

4. _____

_____

5. _____

_____

▶ **Write three sentences about what the javelinas might have done after they trapped the coyote. Use helping verbs and main verbs.**

6. _____

_____

7. _____

_____

8. _____

_____

Harcourt

▶ **Circle the main verb in each sentence.**

   1. Each javelina traveled a different way.

   2. The coyote ran quickly and quietly.

   3. What did the coyote say?

   4. He will blow the tumbleweed house away.

▶ **Complete each sentence with *have* or *has*.**

   5. The woman _____ gathered saguaro ribs.

   6. The two brothers _____ escaped into the desert.

   7. Their sister _____ completed her house.

   8. The three javelinas _____ trapped the coyote.

▶ **Write *compound subject* or *compound predicate* to describe each sentence. Circle the action verbs.**

   9. A woman and a man helped the little javelinas.

     _____

  10. The coyote huffed and puffed.

     _____

  11. He saw the house and smelled the javelina inside.

     _____

  12. The first house and the second house blew over.

     _____

Subjects and Predicates
Action Verbs; Main and Helping Verbs

Harcourt

Name _____

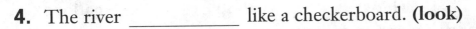

Skill Reminder

- **A present-tense verb** tells about action that is happening now.
- A verb must **agree** with its subject in number.
- Add **-s** or **-es** to most present-tense verbs when the subject of the sentence is *he, she, it,* or a singular noun. Do not add an ending when the subject is *I, you,* or a plural noun.

▶ Underline the verb. Label the subject *S* for singular or *P* for plural.

1. The boss makes a line across the river.

2. Papa follows the line with the ice cutter.

3. They cut the ice into huge, heavy blocks.

▶ Complete each sentence with the correct present-tense form of the verb in parentheses ( ).

4. The river _____ like a checkerboard. **(look)**

5. He _____ the snow on the ice. **(watch)**

6. I _____ about the weather. **(worry)**

7. Papa and Uncle Jacob _____ onto the ice. **(step)**

8. The ship _____ ice to warm countries far away. **(carry)**

▶ Use the verbs *freeze* and *freezes* in sentences of your own.

9. _____

_____

10. _____

Harcourt

▶ **Use the pronouns from the box as subjects of these sentences. Use each pronoun only once. Make sure your subjects and verbs agree.**

I	you	he	she	we	they

1. _____ tap holes in the ice.

2. _____ skates along the river.

3. _____ follow the ice cutter.

4. _____ stops for hot chocolate.

5. _____ shiver in the cold.

6. _____ run indoors.

▶ **Write four sentences. For each sentence, use one present-tense verb from the box.**

ride	rides	gallop	gallops

7. _____

_____

8. _____

_____

9. _____

_____

10. _____

_____

Harcourt

Name _____

▶ **Rewrite the sentences. Replace the underlined words with proper nouns.**

1. The schooner comes one <u>day</u> in December.

   _____

   _____

2. The <u>man</u> walks down to the docks.

   _____

3. Will <u>your aunt</u> make hot chocolate?

   _____

4. I plan to visit <u>that state</u>.

   _____

▶ **Underline the main verb and circle the helping verb in each sentence.**

5. The cacao pods have ripened.

6. Papa has opened a coconut.

7. Mama has roasted the cocoa beans.

8. She and I have crushed the beans.

▶ **Complete each sentence with the correct present-tense form of the verb in parentheses ( ).**

9. The bag _____ like pine trees. (**smell**)

10. The sailors _____ ice for cocoa beans. (**trade**)

11. Papa _____ me onto the ship. (**carry**)

12. Jacob _____ me pictures of Maine. (**show**)

Common and Proper Nouns
Main and Helping Verbs; Present-Tense Verbs

Skill Reminder

- **A past-tense verb** tells about action that happened in the past.
- **Add *-ed* to most present-tense verbs to make them show past time.**

▶ **Draw one line under the present-tense verbs. Draw two lines under the past-tense verbs.**

1. Cowboys depend on their horses.

2. That palomino pony jumped up.

3. The pony begged for apples.

▶ **Complete each sentence with the correct past-tense form of the verb in parentheses ( ).**

4. The rider _____ toward the black horse. **(walk)**

5. A spotted pony _____ nearby. **(graze)**

6. The cowboy _____ into the saddle. **(hop)**

7. The horse _____ **(whinny)**

8. Then it _____ around the corral. **(trot)**

▶ **Use the past-tense form of each verb below in a sentence of your own.**

9. follow _____

10. skip _____

Harcourt

▶ **Rewrite this present-tense paragraph in the past tense.**

The horses sniff the air as storm clouds float overhead. Suddenly raindrops pour down. Thunderclaps scare the horses. They press against the fence.

1.–5. _____

_____

_____

_____

_____

_____

▶ **Write the past-tense form of the underlined present-tense verb in each sentence.**

6. The cowboys <u>carry</u> their plates to Cookie. _____

7. The flapjacks <u>cook</u> quickly. _____

8. The cooks <u>flip</u> them over. _____

9. They <u>fry</u> eggs and bacon, too. _____

10. The eggs and bacon <u>taste</u> great. _____

11. After breakfast, the cooks <u>nap</u>. _____

12. Meanwhile, the cowboys <u>wash</u> the dishes. _____

Harcourt

▶ **Rewrite each sentence. Use a singular or plural pronoun to replace the underlined word(s).**

1. <u>Grandmother</u> waited for us at the ranch house.

   _____

2. <u>Dad</u> cuts wood for a new fence.

   _____

3. <u>The cowhands</u> played games every day.

   _____

4. We waved to <u>the Smithson family</u> at the rodeo.

   _____

▶ **Underline each verb. Then rewrite present-tense verbs as past-tense verbs. Rewrite past-tense verbs as present-tense verbs. Make sure that each present-tense verb you write agrees with its subject.**

5. Some ranch hands chop firewood. _____

6. The trail boss lived on a ranch. _____

7. Cowhands use lariats. _____

8. The point riders tried a different trail. _____

9. The cook planned the meals. _____

10. Wranglers care for the horses. _____

11. The cowboys hurry into town. _____

12. One rancher purchased new clothes. _____

Singular and Plural Pronouns
Present-Tense Verbs; Past-Tense Verbs

Harcourt

Name_____

Skill Reminder

An **irregular verb** does not end with *-ed* in the past tense.

▶ Complete the chart with the correct form of each verb.

VERB	PRESENT	PAST	PAST WITH HELPING VERB
1. come	come, comes	came	(have, has, had) _____
2. do	do, does	_____	(have, has, had) done
3. have	have, has	_____	(have, has, had) had
4. say	say, says	_____	(have, has, had) said
5. see	see, sees	saw	(have, has, had) _____

▶ Complete each sentence with the correct past-tense or helping-verb form of the verb in parentheses ( ).

6. We _____ home from the bank. **(come)**

7. We had _____ a $1,000 bill. **(see)**

8. "That is a lot of money," you _____ . **(say)**

▶ Choose two past-tense verbs from the chart. Use each one in a sentence.

9. _____

_____

10. _____

Harcourt

Irregular Verbs

Name _____

▶ **Rewrite each sentence, using the correct form of the verb in parentheses ( ).**

1. Karen _____ many chores this month. (*do*—past tense with a helping verb)

_____

2. She _____ to work hard. (*have*—past tense with a helping verb)

_____

3. Karen _____ she keeps her money in the bank. (past tense of *say*)

_____

4. She _____ the new interest rates. (past tense of *see*)

_____

5. She _____ to the bank to deposit more money. (*come*—past tense with a helping verb)

_____

▶ **Rewrite this present-tense story in the past tense.**

The woman comes to the bank teller's window. "I have a check for fifty dollars," she says. "Perhaps you see it on the counter. Do you?"

6.–10. _____

_____

_____

_____

Harcourt

Name _____

▶ **Read the passage and choose the word or group of words that belongs in each space. Fill in the bubble for the correct answer.**

Yesterday a store owner **(1)** _____ to talk to our class. I had **(2)** _____ her

store on College Street. She **(3)** _____ maps and globes. She **(4)** _____ it

was exciting to start a business. She has **(5)** _____ hard to make it a success.

1 ⊖ came

⊖ comes

⊖ coming

⊖ come

2 ⊖ saw

⊖ see

⊖ seeing

⊖ seen

3 ⊖ selles

⊖ selling

⊖ selled

⊖ sells

4 ⊖ sayd

⊖ say

⊖ said

⊖ saying

5 ⊖ tryed

⊖ tried

⊖ tries

⊖ trying

Present-Tense Verbs; Past-Tense Verbs
Irregular Verbs

Name_____

Theme 5 Review

▶ **Circle the action verb in each sentence.**
Underline any helping verbs.

1. Leah rode her pony past Mr. B.'s store.

2. Mama and Papa have sold everything.

3. The neighbors will buy many things.

4. Mr. B. returned Leah's pony.

5. The corn might grow better next year.

▶ **Complete each sentence with *have* or *has*.**

6. The coyote _____ knocked at each door.

7. The javelinas _____ escaped from the coyote.

8. They _____ trapped it in the chimney.

9. The coyote _____ destroyed two houses.

10. The adobe house _____ protected the javelinas.

▶ **Complete each sentence with the correct present-tense form of the verb in parentheses ( ).**

11. The workers _____ huge blocks of ice. **(prepare)**

12. Papa _____ the ice cutter. **(fix)**

Harcourt

Theme 5 Review

13. The sailor _____ off the boat. **(hurry)**

14. Uncle Jacob _____ lunch with us. **(eat)**

15. After lunch, I _____ the dishes. **(wash)**

▶ **Complete each sentence with the correct past-tense form or helping-verb form of the verb in parentheses ( ).**

16. I _____ cattle in the meadow. **(see)**

17. They _____ all morning long. **(graze)**

18. Some cowhands _____ in the afternoon. **(come)**

19. One cowboy _____ his lariat. **(drop)**

20. We _____ for it together. **(look)**

21. I had _____ a lot of work that day. **(do)**

22. My friend Sandra _____ apples for the horses. **(carry)**

23. That wrangler has _____ many cattle drives. **(see)**

24. "It's hard work," he _____ . **(say)**

25. The ranchers have _____ many difficult times. **(have)**

Harcourt

Skill Reminder

An **irregular verb** does not end with -*ed* to show past tense.

▶ Complete the chart with the correct form of each verb.

VERB	PRESENT	PAST	PAST WITH HELPING VERB
1. eat	eat, eats	ate	(have, has, had)
2. give	give, gives		(have, has, had) given
3. go	go, goes		(have, has, had) gone
4. ride	ride, rides		(have, has, had) ridden
5. take	take, takes	took	(have, has, had)

▶ Complete each sentence with the correct past-tense or helping-verb form of the verb in parentheses ( ).

    6. I _____ one apple. **(eat)**

    7. I have _____ the others to Coyote. **(give)**

    8. She _____ some corn and seeds, too. **(take)**

▶ Choose two past-tense verbs from the chart above. Use each one in a sentence.

    9. _____

          _____

    10. _____

Harcourt

Name _____

▶ **Complete the chart with the correct form of each verb.**

VERB	PRESENT	PAST	PAST WITH HELPING VERB
1. see	see, sees	saw	(have, has, had)
2. do	do, does	did	(have, has, had)
3. write	write, writes		(have, has, had) written
4. drive	drive, drives	drove	(have, has, had)
5. ring	ring, rings		(have, has, had) rung

▶ **Rewrite this present-tense story in the past tense.**

I ride my horse into the
desert. We go up a steep hill.
My pony eats grass. I take a
look at the moon. It gives back
a shimmery light.

6.–10. _____

_____

_____

_____

_____

_____

More Irregular Verbs

Name _____

▶ **Complete the chart with the past-tense form of each verb.**

PRESENT	PAST		PRESENT	PAST
1. give			**6.** see	
2. gleam			**7.** slap	
3. gab			**8.** say	
4. go			**9.** skate	
5. gobble			**10.** smile	

▶ **Rewrite each sentence, using the correct helping-verb form of the verb in parentheses ( ).**

11. I had ____**(ride)**____ in a pickup truck.

_____

12. We have ____**(go)**____ to the canyon.

_____

13. The trip has ____**(take)**____ four days.

_____

14. We had never ____**(see)**____ a triple rainbow.

_____

15. They have ____**(tell)**____ us about their trip.

_____

Past-Tense Verbs
Irregular Verbs

Name _____

Skill Reminder

- Forms of the verb *be* link the subject of the sentence to one or more words in the predicate.
- Forms of *be* tell what or where someone or something is or was.
- The subject of the sentence and the form of *be* must agree.

▶ Underline the forms of *be*. Write whether the tense of each is *present* or *past*.

1. A roadrunner is a desert animal. _____

2. Roadrunners were everywhere. _____

3. I am very fond of roadrunners. _____

4. They are strange-looking. _____

5. A roadrunner was in my favorite cartoon. _____

▶ Complete each sentence by adding the form of *be* asked for in parentheses ( ).

6. You _____ in the park zoo. **(present)**

7. He _____ with you. **(present)**

8. We _____ on a field trip. **(past)**

9. I _____ next to the roadrunner cage. **(present)**

10. It _____ near some tumbleweed. **(past)**

Harcourt

The Verb *Be*

Name _____

▶ **Complete the chart with the correct form of *be*.**

PRESENT	PAST
1. I	**6.** I
2. you	**7.** you
3. it	**8.** it
4. we	**9.** we
5. they	**10.** they

▶ **Rewrite this past-tense story in the present tense.**

Alejandro was content. The animals were happy at their water hole. They were glad Alejandro was their friend. I was glad, too.

11.–15. _____

_____

_____

_____

_____

_____

_____

The Verb *Be*

Harcourt

Name_____

▶ **Complete the chart. Write the missing form of each verb.**

PRESENT	PAST
1. they have	they _____
2. she _____	she was
3. it says	it _____
4. we go	we _____
5. they _____	they were

▶ **Rewrite each sentence. Change present-tense verbs to past tense. Change past-tense verbs to present tense.**

6. Visitors were welcome at Alejandro's house.

_____

7. It is a small adobe house.

_____

8. Alejandro had a beautiful garden.

_____

9. We ride by in a pickup truck.

_____

10. I was happy in the desert.

_____

11. Some desert animals ate plants.

_____

12. You see many kinds of plants there.

_____

Irregular Verbs
The Verb *Be*

Name _____

Skill Reminder

- **A contraction** is a short way to write two words. An apostrophe takes the place of the missing letter or letters.
- Subject pronouns and the negative *not* are often used in contractions with verbs.

▶ **Write the two words that make up each contraction.**

1. Aren't mountains interesting? _____

2. You're looking at Mount Everest. _____

3. Surprisingly, it's still growing. _____

4. Don't mountains ever stop growing? _____

5. No, they aren't as still as they seem. _____

▶ **Write the contraction for each word pair.**

6. he is _____   **8.** I am _____

7. they are _____   **9.** we are _____

▶ **Rewrite each sentence. Use a contraction in place of the underlined words.**

10. Most people <u>can not</u> climb tall mountains.

_____

11. Mount Everest <u>has not</u> proved easy to climb.

_____

12. I <u>would not</u> dare to try it.

_____

Contractions

Harcourt

▶ **Find the "sums." Write the contractions.**

1. could + not = _____

2. had + not = _____

3. they + are = _____

4. I + am = _____

5. have+ not = _____

6. are + not = _____

7. she + is = _____

8. we + are = _____

9. is + not = _____

10. did + not = _____

▶ **Rewrite this paragraph. Replace each contraction with the two words used to form it.**

The wind isn't kind to rocks. Slowly, it's wearing them down. They're taking on new shapes. Don't be alarmed. You're seeing nature in action.

11.–15. _____

_____

_____

_____

_____

Harcourt

▶ **Write the two words that make up each contraction. Then circle the subject pronouns and underline the forms of *be* in your answers.**

1. We're going to study earthquakes. _____

2. Let me know when you're ready. _____

3. It's a long way to the library. _____

4. Dad says he's going to drive us. _____

5. I'm looking forward to learning more. _____

▶ **Rewrite each sentence. Replace the underlined words with contractions.**

6. I am doing a report about the Himalayas.

   _____

   _____

7. They are discussed in that book about mountains.

   _____

   _____

8. You will learn a lot from my report.

   _____

   _____

9. I would not want to climb Mount Everest.

   _____

   _____

10. It is very dangerous.

   _____

Harcourt

Subject Pronouns
The Verb *Be*; Contractions

Name _____

Skill Reminder

- **An adverb is a word that describes a verb.**
- **An adverb may tell *where, when,* or *how* an action happens.**

▶ **Write the adverb that describes each underlined verb.**

1. The armadillo often <u>sends</u> postcards. _____

2. He <u>jots</u> down his thoughts. _____

3. The little animal <u>writes</u> beautifully. _____

4. He <u>mailed</u> one postcard today. _____

5. The postal carrier <u>took</u> it away. _____

▶ **Tell whether the underlined adverb tells *where, when,* or *how.***

6. The armadillo sits <u>thoughtfully</u>. _____

7. He <u>then</u> begins a letter. _____

8. He <u>carefully</u> chooses some paper. _____

9. He writes his address <u>there</u>. _____

10. <u>Finally</u>, he finishes his work. _____

▶ **Rewrite each sentence. Add an adverb that gives the information in parentheses ( ).**

11. I received a letter. **(when)**

_____

12. The postal carrier delivered it. **(where)**

_____

▶ **Read Brillo Armadillo's postcard. Circle the adverbs. Underline the verbs they describe.**

1.–5.

Dear Sasparillo,

You write beautifully. Your stories interest me greatly. Next, tell me about Texas. You clearly love it. Visit me sometime!

Your friend,

Brillo

▶ **Rewrite Sasparillo's postcard to make it more interesting. Add an adverb to describe each underlined verb.**

Dear Brillo,

I love Texas. The mountains tower. The desert blooms. Eagles fly. Write to me!

Your friend,

Sasparillo

6.–10. _____

_____

_____

_____

_____

Harcourt